# GO FLY A KITE, CHARLIE BROWN

## Books by Charles M. Schulz

Weekly Reader Children's Book Club presents

# GO FLY A KITE, CHARLIE BROWN

## A NEW PEANUTS BOOK

## by Charles M. Schulz

**HOLT, RINEHART AND WINSTON**
**New York • Chicago • San Francisco**

**Published, August, 1960**

Published simultaneously in Canada by
Holt, Rinehart and Winston of Canada, Limited

ISBN: 0-03-029950-0

Library of Congress Catalog Card Number 60-5911

Weekly Reader Children's Book Club Edition

FOR ME THIS BLANKET PROVIDES ALL THE SECURITY OF A GOOD INSURANCE PROGRAM

DID YOU NOTICE THAT I CUT A LITTLE PIECE OUT OF YOUR BLANKET, LINUS? I HAD TO MAKE A QUILT FOR MY DOLL'S BED... I HOPE YOU WON'T MIND...

GOOD GRIEF!

YOU JUST PUT A HOLE IN MY ANNUITY!

SCHULZ

---

I THINK IT'S TIME TO GO HOME AND TAKE A SHOWER..

GOING TO GET ALL CLEANED UP, EH, "PIG-PEN"?

WELL, I'VE LEARNED NEVER TO EXPECT TOO MUCH FROM A SHOWER...

I HAVE TO BE SATISFIED IF IT JUST SETTLES THE DUST!

SCHULZ

SOMETIMES WHEN I GET UP IN THE MORNING, I FEEL VERY PECULIAR..

I FEEL LIKE I'VE JUST **GOT** TO BITE A CAT! I FEEL LIKE IF I DON'T BITE A CAT BEFORE SUNDOWN, I'LL GO CRAZY!!

BUT THEN I JUST TAKE A DEEP BREATH AND FORGET ABOUT IT..

THAT'S WHAT IS KNOWN AS REAL **MATURITY!**

SCHULZ

CHARLIE BROWN WHAT WOULD BE YOUR REACTION IF SOMEONE SAID YOU COULD HAVE YOUR LIFE OVER AGAIN?

YOU MEAN EXACTLY AS I'VE LIVED IT? NO CHANGES? EVERYTHING HAPPENING JUST THE WAY IT DID BEFORE?

UH HUH...WHAT WOULD BE YOUR REACTION?

# AAAUGHH!

SCHULZ

IN THE OLDEN DAYS THIS WAS KNOWN AS BRINGING THE WARRIOR HOME ON HIS SHIELD!

---

ONCE YOU'VE GOT A KITE IN THE AIR, CHARLIE BROWN, IS IT ANY TROUBLE GETTING IT DOWN AGAIN?

WHAM!

THAT'S ONE PROBLEM I'VE NEVER HAD TO WORRY ABOUT

HE'S GREAT, I TELL YOU... REALLY GREAT!

REMEMBER HOW HE USED TO SWAT THE OL' HORSEHIDE LAST SUMMER?

WELL, YOU HAVEN'T SEEN ANYTHING UNTIL YOU'VE SEEN HIM KICK THAT PIGSKIN!

WHY CAN'T THEY JUST PLAY THEIR OL' GAMES, AND LEAVE THE ANIMALS OUT OF IT?

SCHULZ

I OWE YOU AN APOLOGY "PIG-PEN"! I'VE BEEN TEASING YOU A LOT LATELY..

BUT WHO AM I TO TEASE YOU? YOU MAY BE DIRTY, BUT AT LEAST YOU HAVE CHARACTER!

ME? I'M **BLAH**! THAT'S JUST WHAT I AM..**BLAH**! I'M COMPLETELY **BLAH**! I WAS BORN **BLAH**, AND I'LL DIE **BLAH**!

WHEN YOU'RE LOOKING AT **ME**, YOU'RE LOOKING AT THE ALL-TIME NUMBER-ONE CHAMPION **BLAH**!!

SCHULZ

---

SNOWFLAKES FASCINATE ME... MILLIONS OF THEM FALLING GENTLY TO THE GROUND..

AND THEY SAY THAT NO TWO OF THEM ARE ALIKE!

EACH ONE COMPLETELY DIFFERENT FROM ALL THE OTHERS ....

THE LAST OF THE RUGGED INDIVIDUALISTS!

SAY, I DO! I DO!! I DO!!!

NOPE, I GUESS I DON'T...

..IT'S JUST A LITTLE DIRT..

?

FOR ONE BRIEF, EXCITING MOMENT I THOUGHT I NEEDED A SHAVE!

ALL RIGHT! SO IT'S SUPPERTIME!

I **KNOW** IT'S SUPPERTIME! I'LL BE WITH YOU AS SOON AS THIS PROGRAM IS OVER!

NOW JUST SIT STILL, AND ENJOY THE SHOW...

SIGH

SCHULZ

CHARLIE BROWN, WE NEED YOUR ADVICE...

SAY A PERSON HAS A BAG OF CANDY, AND HALF OF THE PIECES HAVE COCONUT IN THEM.. SAY THE PERSON SHE IS GOING TO SHARE THEM WITH CAN'T STAND COCONUT..

DOES HE HAVE TO ACCEPT THE COCONUT ONES ALONG WITH THE OTHERS IF HE THINKS SHE IS TRYING TO GET RID OF THEM BECAUSE SHE DOESN'T LIKE THEM EITHER?

I HAVE NEVER PRETENDED TO BE ABLE TO SOLVE MORAL ISSUES!

SCHULZ

CHARLIE BROWN, DO YOU THINK THAT SANTA CLAUS REALLY KNOWS HIS JOB?

OH, YES... AFTER ALL, HE'S BEEN AT IT FOR A LONG TIME..

THAT'S JUST WHAT HAS ME WORRIED...

PERHAPS IT'S TIME FOR A **YOUNGER** MAN TO TAKE OVER!

THIS ROCKET BUSINESS IS FASCINATING

EVERY DAY THEY SEEM TO COME UP WITH SOMETHING NEW

FOR AWHILE THEY WERE SENDING UP DOGS... NOW THEY'RE SENDING UP MICE..

THAT'S A VERY HEALTHY TREND!

SCHULZ

SO CHARLIE BROWN HAD A BABY SISTER LAST NIGHT!

BOY, THERE SURE WAS A LOT OF EXCITEMENT AROUND HERE ABOUT MIDNIGHT...PEOPLE RUNNING IN ALL DIRECTIONS...

..CARS COMING AND GOING.. TELEPHONES RINGING...THINGS STILL HAVEN'T CALMED DOWN..

SCHULZ

AND IN ALL THE EXCITEMENT, NOBODY HAS REMEMBERED TO FEED THE DOG!

SO YOU HAVE A NEW BABY SISTER, HUH, CHARLIE BROWN?

YES, AND I'M SO HAPPY...

HAPPY?

I SUPPOSE IT'S NEVER OCCURRED TO YOU THAT OVER-POPULATION IS A SERIOUS PROBLEM?!

SCHULZ

I DON'T THINK IT'S RIGHT TO BRING NEW BABIES INTO THIS UNCERTAIN WORLD...THIS IS THE WRONG TIME!

WHAT ARE YOU GONNA DO WITH ALL THOSE BABIES WHO ARE LINED UP WAITING TO BE BORN?

YOU JUST CAN'T TELL THEM TO GO AWAY AND **WAIT** FOR ANOTHER THOUSAND YEARS, CAN YOU? **CAN YOU?**

NO, I GUESS YOU CAN'T..

THE WHOLE TROUBLE WITH YOU IS YOU NEVER THINK THESE THINGS THROUGH!

YOU KNOW, SNOOPY..HAVING A BABY SISTER IS KIND OF NICE...

I DON'T THINK I'LL FEEL SO ALONE ANY MORE..

WELL, I HOPE HE'S RIGHT, BUT I WOULDN'T KNOW...I NEVER HAD ANY SISTERS OR BROTHERS

I WAS AN ONLY DOG!

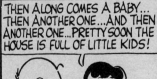

..AND FIVE IS TWENTY-TWO..

NINETEEN HUNDRED AND FIFTY NINE PLUS TWENTY-TWO IS NINETEEN HUNDRED AND EIGHTY-ONE

WHEN I'M TWENTY-TWO AND SALLY IS SEVENTEEN, DO YOU THINK SHE'LL GO OUT WITH ME?

---

THIS HAVING A BABY SISTER MAY DO A LOT FOR CHARLIE BROWN..

IT'S JUST LIABLE TO MAKE HIM INTO A NEW PERSON!

THAT'S A FRIGHTENING THOUGHT...

I CAN THINK OF NOTHING IN ALL THIS WORLD MORE OBNOXIOUS THAN A WELL-ADJUSTED CHARLIE BROWN!

YOU THINK HAVING A BABY SISTER IS GREAT, DON'T YOU?

FROM NOW ON YOU'RE GOING TO HAVE TO **SHARE** THE AFFECTION OF YOUR MOTHER AND DAD! BUT YOU THINK YOU WON'T MIND THAT, DON'T YOU?

YOU THINK IT'LL BE FIFTY-FIFTY, DON'T YOU? WELL, IT WON'T! WITH A BABY SISTER, IT'LL BE FIFTY ONE-FORTY NINE! MAYBE EVEN **SIXTY-FORTY**!!

I'LL BET YOU DIDN'T REALIZE THAT FAMILY LIFE WAS SO MATHEMATICAL!

---

YOU'RE SO SWEET, SNOOPY.. I WISH I COULD GIVE YOU A BIG KISS, BUT OF COURSE, I CAN'T...

SCHULZ

THE CURSE OF A FUZZY FACE!

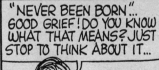

LOOK, THIS IS **YOUR** BABY, NOT MINE! I HAVE MY OWN BABY SISTER AT HOME!

**YOU** WERE THE ONE WHO PUT THE BONNET ON HIM... NOW **YOU** TAKE CARE OF HIM!

I'M NOT INTERESTED ANY MORE.. I HAVE OTHER THINGS TO DO!

YOU'RE A POOR EXCUSE FOR A MOTHER!!

MAMA!

SCHULZ

HERE, SNOOPY, LET ME TAKE THAT STUPID BONNET OFF YOUR HEAD..

THERE!

BOY, I'M GLAD THAT SILLY BUSINESS IS OVER..

I WASN'T SURE WHETHER I WAS GOING TO END UP IN AN ORPHANAGE OR AT THE HUMANE SOCIETY!

SNOOPY

SCHULZ

---

BOY, IT'S TOUGH TO BE A DOG WHEN IT RAINS!

OF COURSE, I'M LUCKIER THAN A LOT OF DOGS.... AT LEAST I HAVE A DOG HOUSE TO GO HOME TO...

---

MOM'S GOING DOWNTOWN, LINUS... DO YOU WANT HER TO GET YOU ANYTHING?

TELL HER I NEED A NEW COWBOY HAT...

WHAT SIZE?

MEDIOCRE!

I'M THE KIND OF PERSON WHO IS KIND OF HARD TO GET TO KNOW I GUESS..

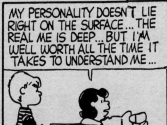
MY PERSONALITY DOESN'T LIE RIGHT ON THE SURFACE... THE REAL ME IS DEEP... BUT I'M WELL WORTH ALL THE TIME IT TAKES TO UNDERSTAND ME...

IN OTHER WORDS, TO KNOW ME, IS TO LOVE ME!

SCHULZ

* SIGH *

I GUESS I LET TOO MANY THINGS BOTHER ME ...

I SEEM TO GET UPSET BY ANY LITTLE THING I HEAR

I THINK I'M GOING TO HAVE TO ERECT SORT OF A MENTAL FENCE TO KEEP UNPLEASANT NEWS OUT OF MY MIND...

DON'T MAKE IT A PICKET FENCE... THEY'RE AWFULLY HARD TO PAINT!

SCHULZ

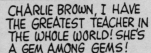

I'M INCLINED TO AGREE WITH YOU, CHARLIE BROWN..

BUT ON THE OTHER HAND WE MUST BE CAUTIOUS IN OUR THINKING...

WE MUST BE CAREFUL NOT TO "THROW OUT THE BABY WITH THE BATH"

PLEASE PARDON THE EXPRESSION

BLAUGH!

CHLORINE!

---

WELL! THE FIRST FALLING LEAF OF THE SEASON...

THE FIRST LEAF TO MAKE THE COURAGEOUS LEAP! THE FIRST LEAF TO DEPART FROM HOME! THE FIRST LEAF TO PLUNGE INTO THE UNKNOWN!

THE FIRST LEAF TO DIE!!

HI LEAF!

LINUS SAID THAT MISS OTHMAR REALLY SPOKE OUT AGAINST BLANKETS TODAY...

SHE SAID THAT IF A CHILD DRAGGED A BLANKET AROUND WITH HIM, IT WAS A SIGN OF IMMATURITY, AND SHE SAID THAT SHE WOULD NEVER PUT UP WITH THAT!

WOW!! THAT MEANS HE'S GOING TO HAVE TO CHOOSE BETWEEN HIS BLANKET AND MISS OTHMAR, DOESN'T IT?

WHO'S MISS OTHMAR?

BUTTERFLIES LIKE ME!

SCHULZ

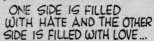

WELL, DID YOU REMEMBER TO BRING THE EGG SHELLS TODAY, LINUS?

AS SOON AS I WOKE UP THIS MORNING, I THOUGHT TO MYSELF, "HAVE MOM SAVE THE EGG SHELLS WHEN SHE FIXES BREAKFAST!"

SO?

SO TODAY WE HAD COLD CEREAL!

SCHULZ

MISS OTHMAR GOT QUITE UPSET WHEN I TOLD HER I FORGOT THE EGG SHELLS AGAIN TODAY...

SHE TURNED SORT OF PALE AND PUT HER HEAD DOWN ON THE DESK...I THINK SHE MAY EVEN HAVE CRIED A LITTLE...

POOR MISS OTHMAR...I HOPE SHE DOESN'T BECOME ILL...

I NEVER REALIZED IT BEFORE, BUT A SCHOOL TEACHER IS A VERY DELICATE INSTRUMENT!

SCHULZ

..AMEN!

AND PLEASE DON'T LET MISS OTHMAR CRACK UP..

LOOK, CHARLIE BROWN! I FINALLY REMEMBERED THE EGG SHELLS!

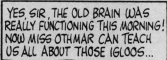

YES, SIR, THE OLD BRAIN WAS REALLY FUNCTIONING THIS MORNING! NOW MISS OTHMAR CAN TEACH US ALL ABOUT THOSE IGLOOS...

TODAY IS SATURDAY!

WHAT'S THIS ABOUT YOU AND YOUR TEACHER AND SOME EGG SHELLS?

MISS OTHMAR WANTS US TO BRING SOME EGG SHELLS TO SCHOOL TO MAKE IGLOOS, BUT I KEEP FORGETTING...SHE'S VERY UPSET

IT'S JUST LIKE YOU... I'VE NEVER KNOWN ANYONE WHO COULD FORGET THINGS WITH SUCH CLOCKLIKE REGULARITY!

I GUESS I'M JUST MECHANICALLY MINDED!

POOR MISS OTHMAR..

I HAD TO GO AND FORGET THE EGG SHELLS AGAIN TODAY.. FOR A MINUTE I THOUGHT SHE WAS GOING TO PASS OUT!

SHE WAS REALLY UPSET HUH?

I'LL SAY!

SHE HAD A PIECE OF CHALK IN HER HAND AND WHEN IT SNAPPED, IT SOUNDED LIKE A RIFLE SHOT!

*SIGH*

I GUESS I JUST DON'T UNDERSTAND DOGS!

?

I CAN'T IMAGINE WHY THEY WANT AN OLD BARE BONE...

SNOOPY'S HAD **THAT** BONE FOR MONTHS, AND YOU NEVER SEE HIM CHEWING ON IT!!

HAS HE NEVER HEARD OF A CONVERSATION PIECE?

SCHROEDER, YOU'LL BE PROUD OF THE PUBLICITY JOB I'VE DONE!

I'VE TOLD EVERYONE I KNOW ABOUT BEETHOVEN'S BIRTHDAY BEING THIS WEDNESDAY...

JUST THINK, ALL OVER THE COUNTRY PEOPLE WILL BE GATHERED TO RAISE TOASTS, AND SING THEIR BEST WISHES...

"HAPPY BIRTHDAY, KARL BEETHOVEN!!"

OH. NO!

LOOK, LUCY, PERHAPS YOU SHOULD KNOW THAT BEETHOVEN'S NAME WASN'T KARL... IT WAS....

OH, NOW YOU'RE GOING TO START PICKING ON ME HUH? AFTER ALL I'VE DONE FOR YOU! TRAMPING THE STREETS, RINGING DOORBELLS...

TALKING TO HUNDREDS OF PEOPLE, TELLING THEM ABOUT BEETHOVEN'S BIRTHDAY!

BUT DO I GET THANKED FOR IT? NO! ALL I GET IS CRITICISM!!!

GOOD GRIEF!

GUESS WHAT HAPPENED, CHARLIE BROWN!

I FINALLY REMEMBERED THE EGG SHELLS! I BROUGHT THEM TO SCHOOL, AND GUESS WHAT!

MISS OTHMAR WAS GONE!!! SHE'S QUIT HER JOB! SHE'S GOING TO GET MARRIED!!!!

I KNEW THE EGG SHELLS WERE ONLY A MANIFESTATION OF A DEEPER PROBLEM!

WHAT IN THE WORLD ARE YOU DOING?

I'M GOING TO SEND MISS OTHMAR A WEDDING PRESENT...

WELL, THAT'S VERY THOUGHTFUL OF YOU, LINUS....WHAT ARE YOU SENDING HER?

A BOX OF EGG SHELLS!

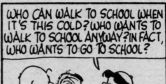

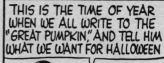

WHAT IN THE WORLD ARE YOU DOING?

DON'T YOU KNOW?

THIS IS THE TIME OF YEAR WHEN WE ALL WRITE TO THE "GREAT PUMPKIN," AND TELL HIM WHAT WE WANT FOR HALLOWEEN

THE "GREAT PUMPKIN" **LOVES** LITTLE CHILDREN

I CAN SEE HIM NOW RISING UP OUT OF THE PUMPKIN PATCH WITH HIS BIG BAG OF TOYS!

HALLOWEEN'S COMING, CHARLIE BROWN!

I'VE WRITTEN A LETTER TO THE "GREAT PUMPKIN" TELLING HIM WHAT I WANT HIM TO BRING ME...

IF YOU HAVEN'T WRITTEN TO HIM YET, CHARLIE BROWN, YOU'D BETTER HURRY!

OH, I LOVE THIS TIME OF YEAR! EVERYONE'S SO FULL OF JOY AND GOOD WILL!

WHY DON'T WE GET THE WHOLE GANG TOGETHER, AND GO OUT AND SING PUMPKIN CAROLS?

...AND THEN ON HALLOWEEN NIGHT THE "GREAT PUMPKIN" RISES UP OUT OF THE PUMPKIN PATCH...

..AND HE BRINGS TOYS TO ALL THE GOOD LITTLE CHILDREN IN THE WORLD!

YOU'RE CRAZY!

ALL RIGHT, SO YOU BELIEVE IN SANTA CLAUS, AND I'LL BELIEVE IN THE "GREAT PUMPKIN".

THE WAY I SEE IT, IT DOESN'T MATTER WHAT YOU BELIEVE JUST SO YOU'RE SINCERE!

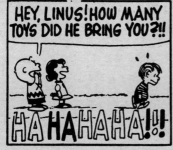

"And so the King was granted his wish..."

"Everything he touched would turn to gold! Now, the next day..."

STOP! YOU DON'T HAVE TO READ ANY FURTHER! I KNOW JUST WHAT'S GOING TO HAPPEN...

THESE THINGS ALWAYS HAVE A WAY OF BACKFIRING!

DEAR SANTA CLAUS,

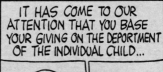

IT HAS COME TO OUR ATTENTION THAT YOU BASE YOUR GIVING ON THE DEPORTMENT OF THE INDIVIDUAL CHILD...

IN OTHER WORDS, YOU JUDGE AS TO WHETHER THE CHILD HAS BEEN GOOD OR BAD...DO YOU REALLY THINK IT IS WISE TO ATTEMPT TO PASS SUCH JUDGMENT?

WHAT IS GOOD? WHAT IS BAD? CAN WE SAY TO OUR NEIGHBOR, "YOU ARE BAD...I AM GOOD"? CAN WE SAY...

OH, BROTHER!

---

TO GO FURTHER INTO THIS MATTER OF THE GIFTS YOU BEAR, DEAR SANTA...

IF, PERCHANCE, YOU JUDGE A LITTLE CHILD AS TOO 'BAD' TO RECEIVE ANY TOYS, ARE YOU NOT ALSO JUDGING HIS PARENTS?

AND IF YOU JUDGE THE PARENTS, THEN ARE YOU NOT ALSO JUDGING THE REMAINDER OF THE FAMILY THE INNOCENT BROTHERS OR SISTERS, AS THE CASE MAY BE?

IN OTHER WORDS DEAR SANTA, MUST I SUFFER FOR THE DEEDS OF...

AH, HA!

SURE, I THINK DOGS SHOULD BE TREATED KINDLY...

I'VE ALWAYS BELIEVED IN BEING KIND TO ANIMALS..

AND I THINK WE SHOULD DO ALL WE CAN TO MAKE OUR PETS HAPPY...

BUT **THIS** IS RIDICULOUS!!

WHERE IN THE WORLD IS LINUS? WE'RE GOING TO BE LATE FOR THE SHOW!

HE BROKE A SHOELACE, AND HAD TO GO BACK TO TRY TO FIND ANOTHER ...

I THINK HE'S TAKING ONE OUT OF HIS DAD'S HUNTING BOOTS..

OKAY, I'M ALL SET TO GO!

I'M SORRY I CAN'T PUSH YOU ANY MORE, SALLY BUT I HAVE TO GO SAVE MY TEAM FROM DEFEAT

HANG ON, TEAM! HERE COMES YOUR FAITHFUL MANAGER!!

I HAD NO IDEA THAT LIFE WAS GOING TO BE FILLED WITH SUCH DRAMA..

HERE COMES GOOD OL' CHARLIE BROWN!

HE MUST BE THROUGH PUSHING HIS BABY SISTER!

YOU'RE JUST IN TIME TO GO IN AS A PINCH-HITTER, OL' BUDDY! YOU CAN SAVE THE GAME, OL' PAL!

REMEMBER, OL' BUDDY, WE'RE COUNTING ON YOU!

BE A HERO, CHARLIE BROWN, OL' PAL!

OR DON'T SHOW YOUR FACE AROUND HERE AGAIN!

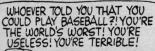

WHOEVER TOLD YOU THAT YOU COULD PLAY BASEBALL?! YOU'RE THE WORLD'S WORST! YOU'RE USELESS! YOU'RE TERRIBLE!

SAY, THIS IS WHERE I LIVE..

OH, YES, SO IT IS...

WELL, DON'T WORRY..I'VE STILL GOT A LITTLE WAY TO GO SO I CAN TAKE OVER...

WHOEVER TOLD YOU THAT YOU COULD PLAY BASEBALL? YOU'RE NO GOOD FOR ANYTHING! YOU'RE WORSE THAN USELESS! YOU'RE WORSE THAN TERRIBLE! YOU'RE..

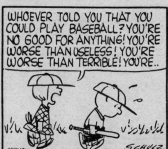

SCHULZ

THIS IS THE WORST YET..I'VE REALLY HIT BOTTOM!

MY MOTHER IS MAD AT ME FOR RUNNING OUT ON MY JOB OF PUSHING MY BABY SISTER AROUND IN HER STROLLER...

AND NOW ALL THE KIDS ARE MAD AT ME FOR STRIKING OUT AND LOSING THE BIGGEST GAME OF THE SEASON!

SUDDENLY I FEEL VERY OLD...

SCHULZ

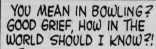

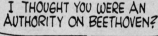

---

LOOK, CHARLIE BROWN! A LETTER FROM MISS OTHMAR!

ONLY HER NAME ISN'T OTHMAR ANY MORE...IT'S MRS. HAGEMEYER! SHE THANKS ME FOR THE EGG SHELLS I SENT, AND SAYS SHE'LL KEEP THEM FOREVER...

AND SHE SAYS SHE MISSES ALL THE KIDS IN HER CLASS, BUT YOU KNOW WHO SHE SAYS SHE MISSES MOST? ME!!

ONLY 28 MORE DAYS UNTIL BEETHOVEN'S BIRTHDAY!

WHERE **DOES** THE TIME GO?

SCHULZ

ALL RIGHT, WHO'S THE WISE GUY?

SCHULZ